TRAVIS
THE MAN WHO

Sony Music Publishing Limited

Exclusive distributors:
Music Sales Limited, 8/9 Frith Street, London W1V 5TZ, England.
Music Sales Pty Limited, 120 Rothschild Avenue, Rosebery, NSW 2018, Australia.

Order No. AM961499
ISBN 0-7119-7897-2
This book © Copyright 1999 by Sony Music Publishing Limited.

Music arranged by Martin Shellard.
Music engraved by Digital Music Art.

Printed in the United Kingdom by Caligraving Limited, Thetford, Norfolk.

Your Guarantee of Quality:
As publishers, we strive to produce every book to the highest commercial standards.
The music has been freshly engraved and has been carefully designed to minimise awkward page turns and to make playing from it a real pleasure.
Particular care has been given to specifying acid-free, neutral-sized paper made from pulps which have not been elemental chlorine bleached.
This pulp is from farmed sustainable forests and was produced with special regard for the environment.
Throughout, the printing and binding have been planned to ensure a sturdy, attractive publication which should give years of enjoyment.
If your copy fails to meet our high standards, please inform us and we will gladly replace it.

Music Sales' complete catalogue describes thousands of titles and
is available in full colour sections by subject, direct from Music Sales Limited.
Please state your areas of interest and send a cheque/postal order for £1.50 for postage to:
Music Sales Limited, Newmarket Road, Bury St. Edmunds, Suffolk IP33 3YB.

www.musicsales.co.uk

Guitar Tablature Explained

Guitar music can be notated three different ways: on a musical stave, in tablature, and in rhythm slashes

RHYTHM SLASHES are written above the stave. Strum chords in the rhythm indicated. Round noteheads indicate single notes.

THE MUSICAL STAVE shows pitches and rhythms and is divided by lines into bars. Pitches are named after the first seven letters of the alphabet.

TABLATURE graphically represents the guitar fingerboard. Each horizontal line represents a string, and each number represents a fret.

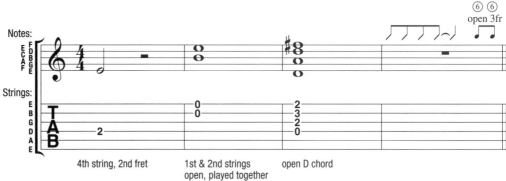

4th string, 2nd fret   1st & 2nd strings open, played together   open D chord

definitions for special guitar notation

SEMI-TONE BEND: Strike the note and bend up a semi-tone (1/2 step).

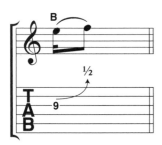

WHOLE-TONE BEND: Strike the note and bend up a whole-tone (whole step).

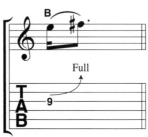

GRACE NOTE BEND: Strike the note and bend as indicated. Play the first note as quickly as possible.

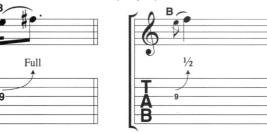

QUARTER-TONE BEND: Strike the note and bend up a 1/4 step.

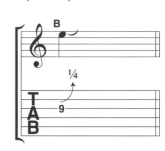

BEND & RELEASE: Strike the note and bend up as indicated, then release back to the original note.

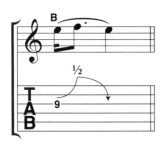

BEND & RESTRIKE: Strike the note and bend as indicated then restrike the string where the symbol occurs.

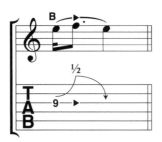

PRE-BEND: Bend the note as indicated, then strike it.

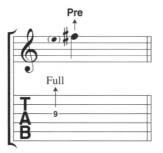

PRE-BEND & RELEASE: Bend the note as indicated. Strike it and release the note back to the original pitch.

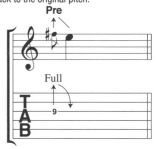

HAMMER-ON: Strike the first (lower) note with one finger, then sound the higher note (on the same string) with another finger by fretting it without picking.

PULL-OFF: Place both fingers on the notes to be sounded. Strike the first note and without picking, pull the finger off to sound the second (lower) note.

LEGATO SLIDE (GLISS): Strike the first note and then slide the same fret-hand finger up or down to the second note. The second note is not struck.

SHIFT SLIDE (GLISS & RESTRIKE): Same as legato slide, except the second note is struck.

NATURAL HARMONIC: Strike the note while the fret-hand lightly touches the string directly over the fret indicated.

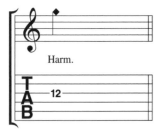

PICK SCRAPE: The edge of the pick is rubbed down (or up) the string, producing a scratchy sound.

PALM MUTING: The note is partially muted by the pick hand lightly touching the string(s) just before the bridge.

MUFFLED STRINGS: A percussive sound is produced by laying the fret hand across the string(s) without depressing, and striking them with the pick hand.

NOTE: The speed of any bend is indicated by the music notation and tempo.

Writing To Reach You

Words & Music by Fran Healy.

Gtrs. 1+3 Capo 2nd fret

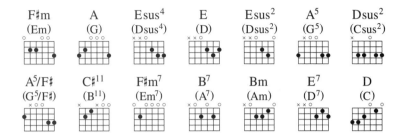

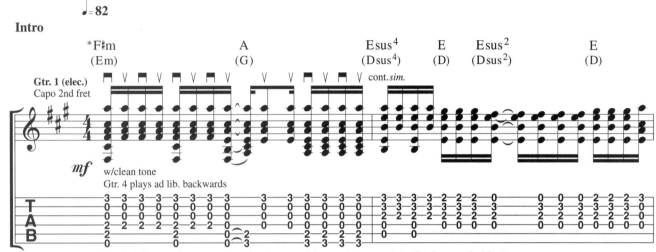

Intro

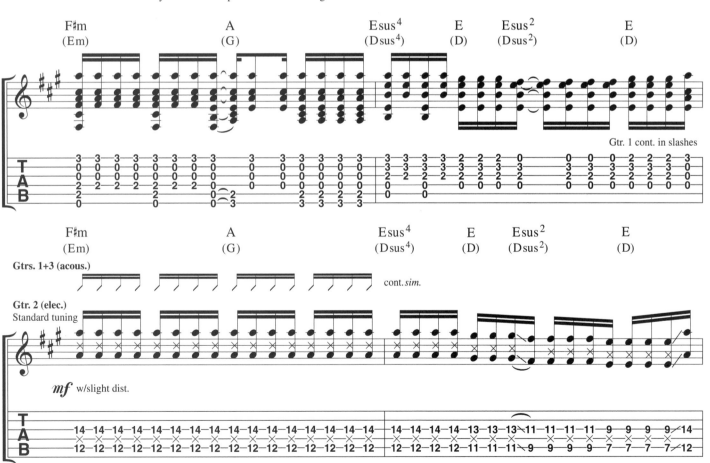

* Symbols in parentheses represent chord names with respect to capoed gtr. (Tab 0 = capo 2nd fret)
  Symbols above represent actual sounding chords

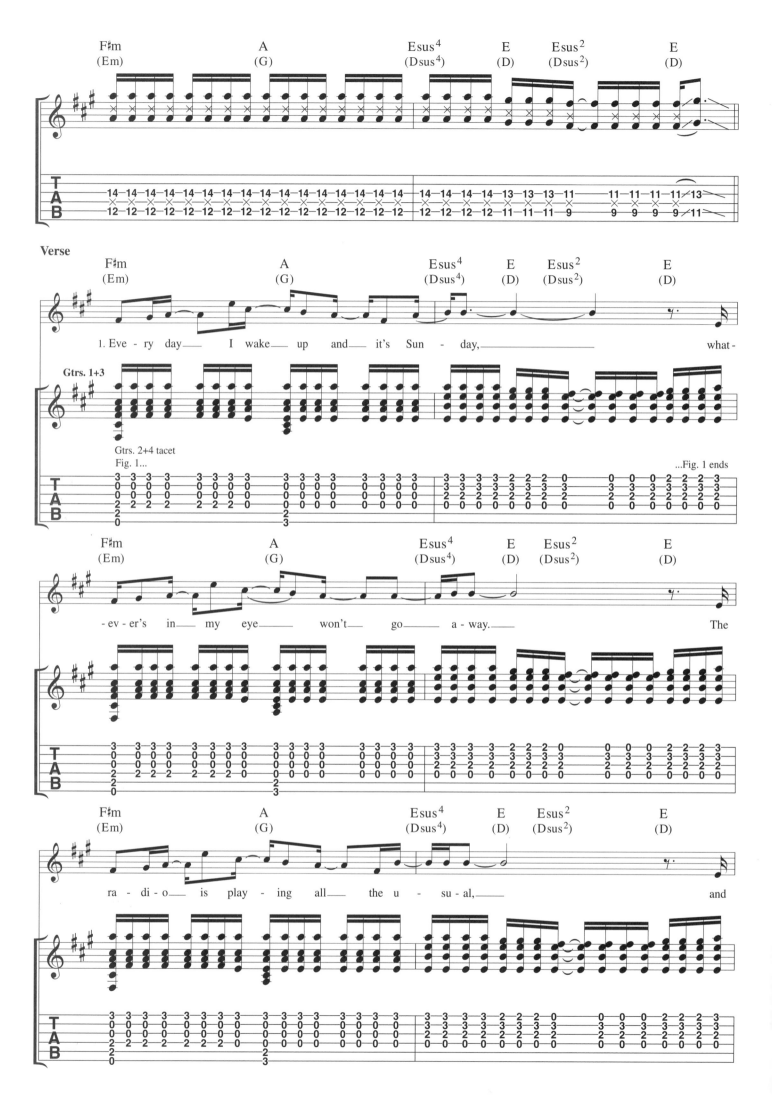

Verse

1. Eve - ry day___ I wake___ up and___ it's Sun - day,_____ what -

-ev - er's in___ my eye___ won't___ go___ a - way.___ The

ra - di - o___ is play - ing all___ the u - su - al,___ and

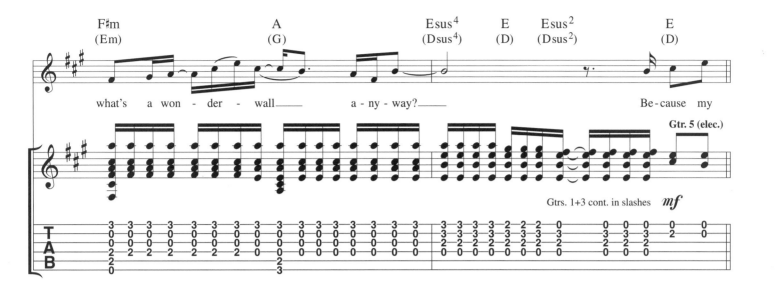

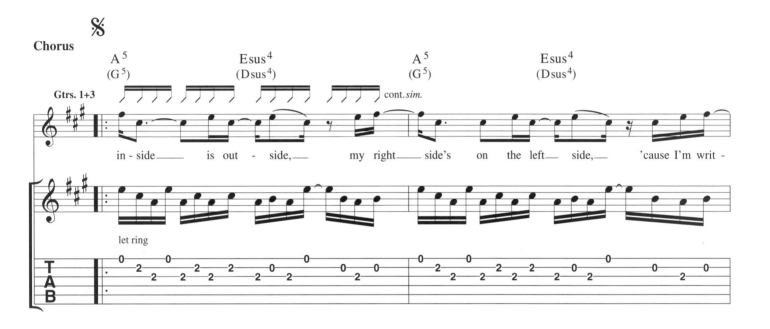

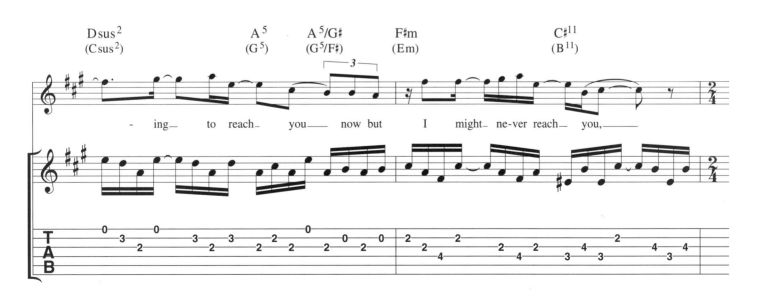

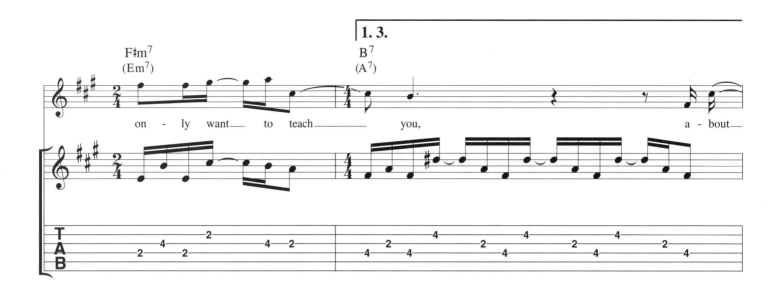

on - ly want_ to teach_ you,_ a - bout_

To Coda ⊕

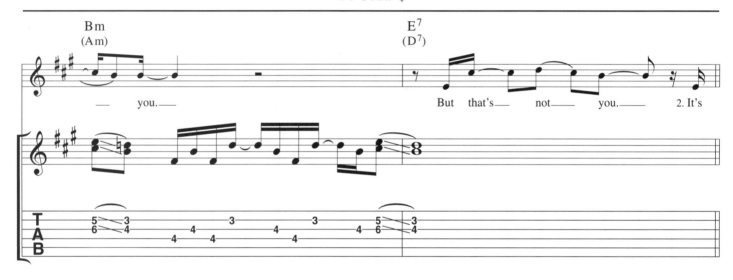

_ you._ But that's_ not_ you._ 2. It's

Verse

good to know_ that you_ are home_ for christ - mas, It's

Gtrs. 1+3 w/Fig. 1   hold- - - -

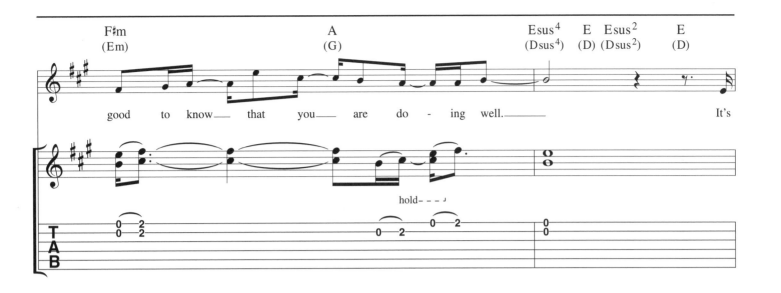

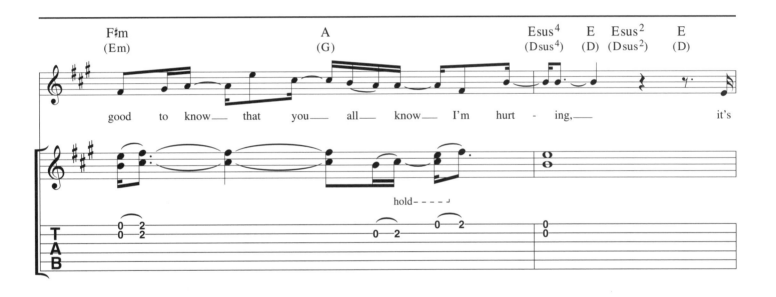

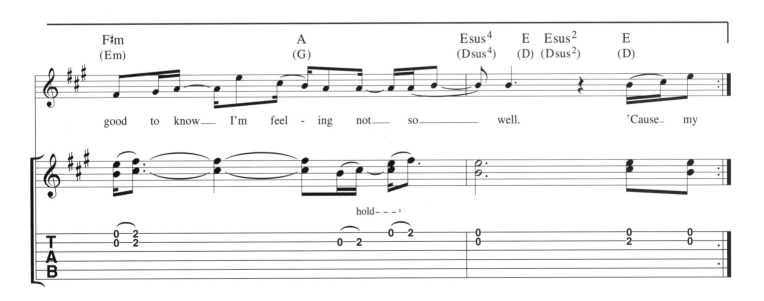

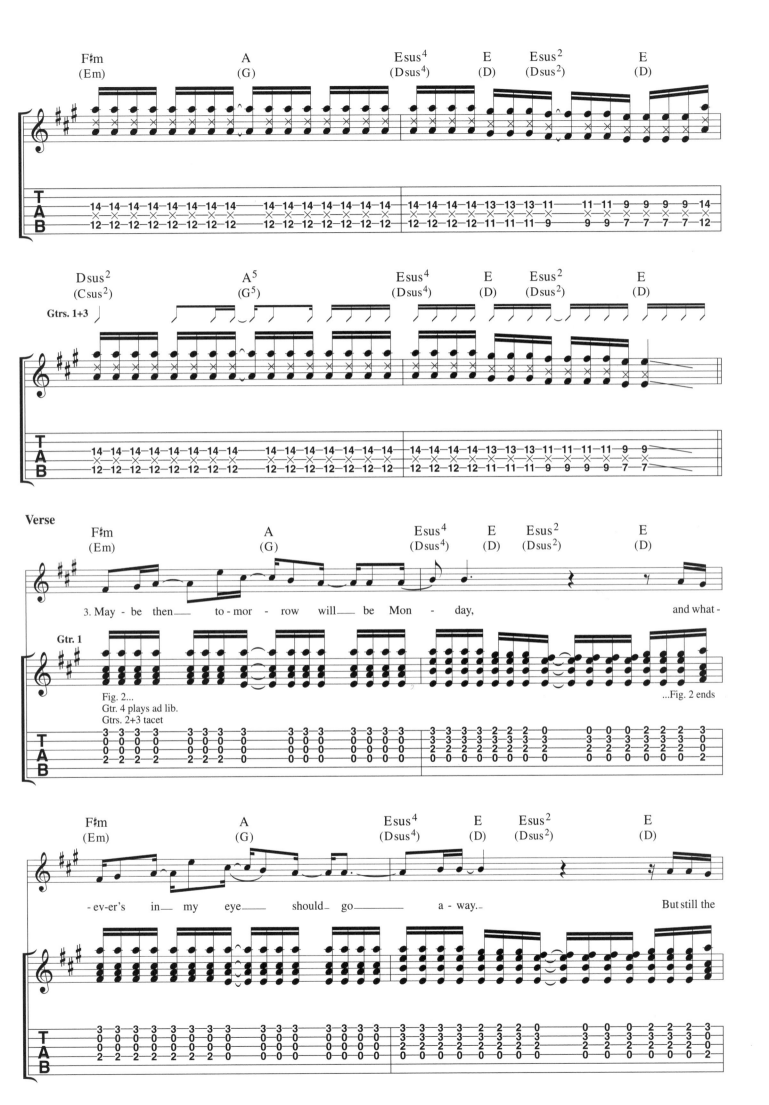

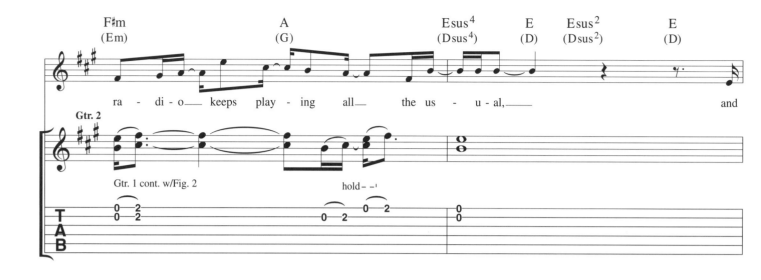

ra - di - o____ keeps play - ing all____ the us - u - al,____ and

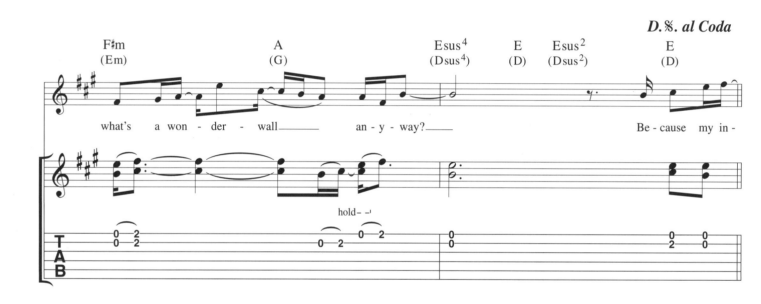

what's a won - der - wall____ an - y - way?____ Be - cause my in -

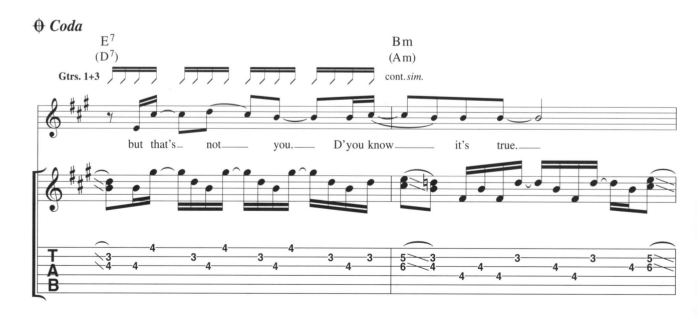

but that's____ not____ you.____ D'you know____ it's true.____

The Fear

Words & Music by Fran Healy.

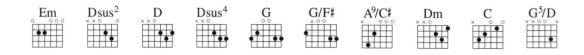

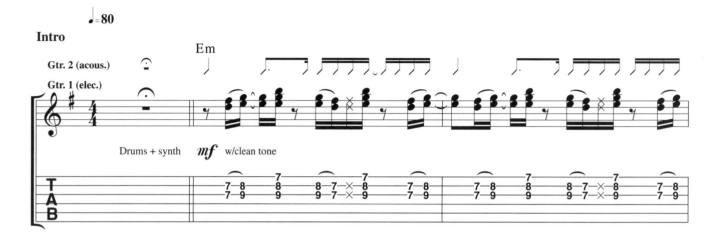

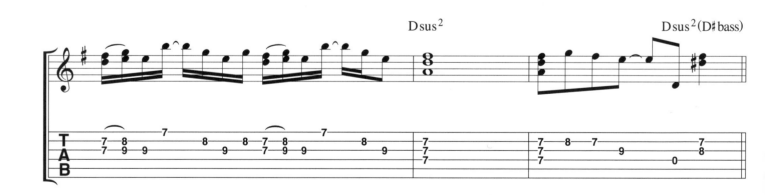

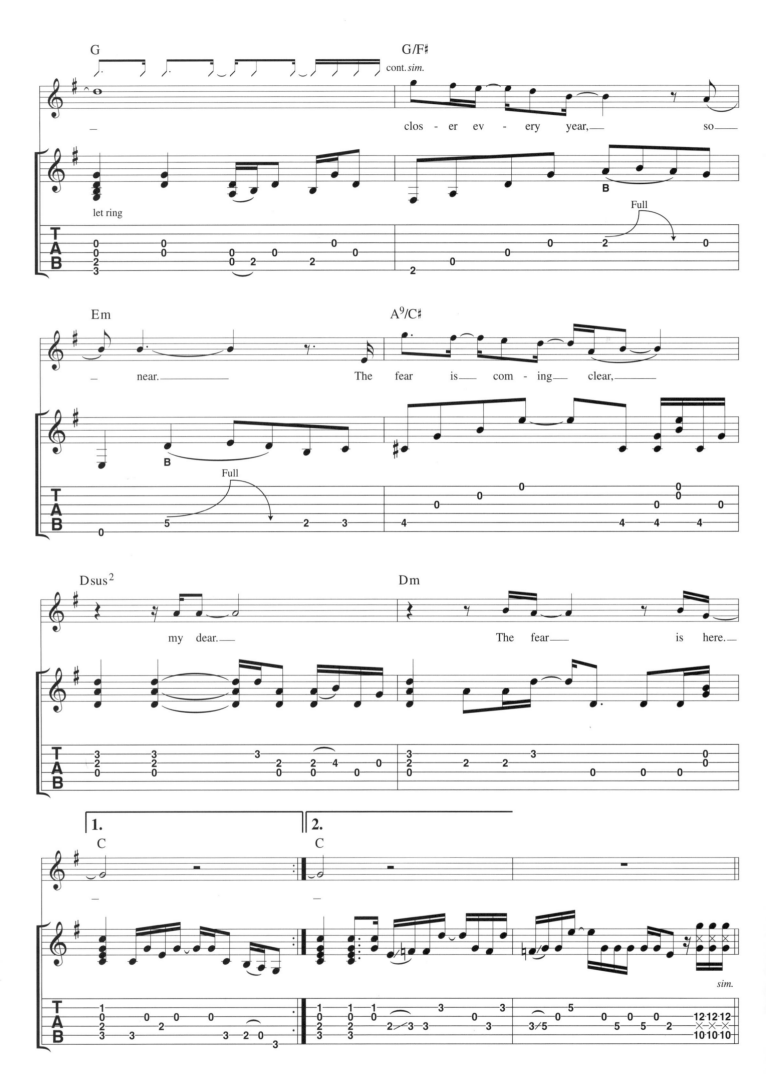

Interlude

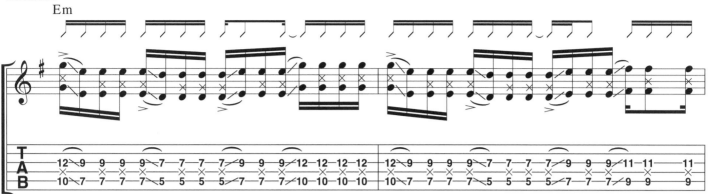

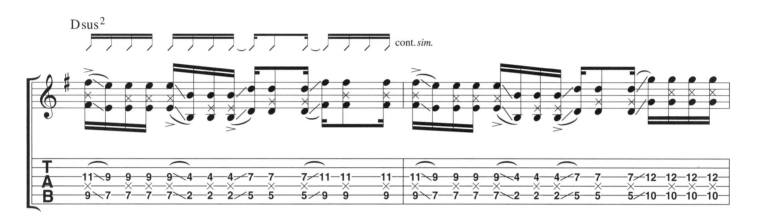

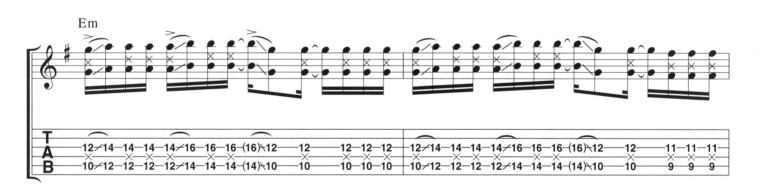

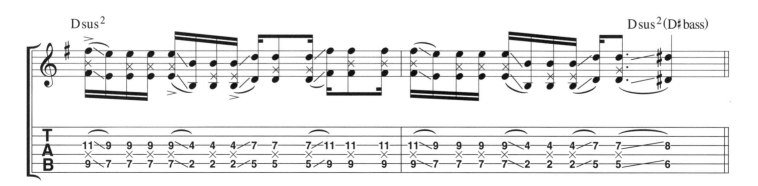

Verse

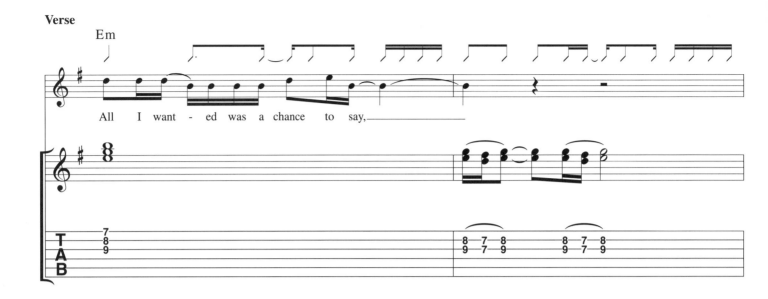

All I want - ed was a chance to say,_____

I would like__ to see you in the morn - ing._____

Roll - ing ov - er just to have you there,_____ would make

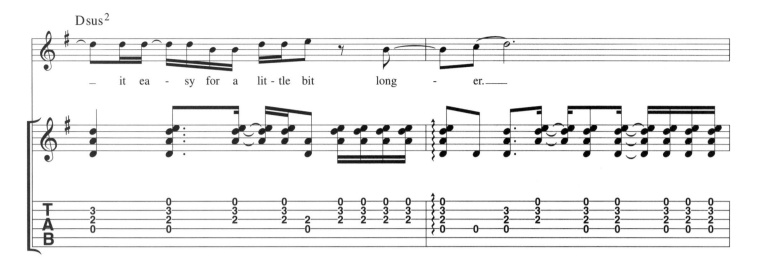

it ea - sy for a lit - tle bit long - er.____

Make it ea - sy for a lit - tle bit long - er.____

Repeat ad lib. to fade

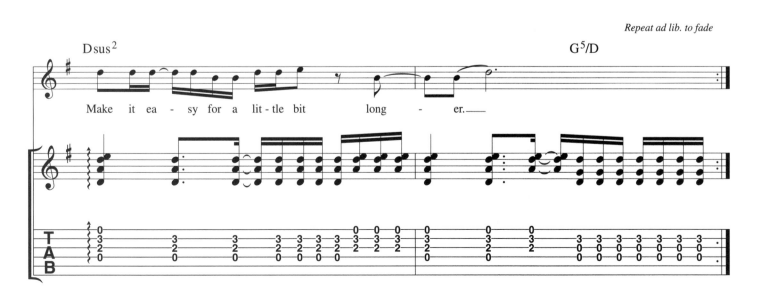

Make it ea - sy for a lit - tle bit long - er.____

As You Are

Words & Music by Fran Healy.

Capo 3rd fret

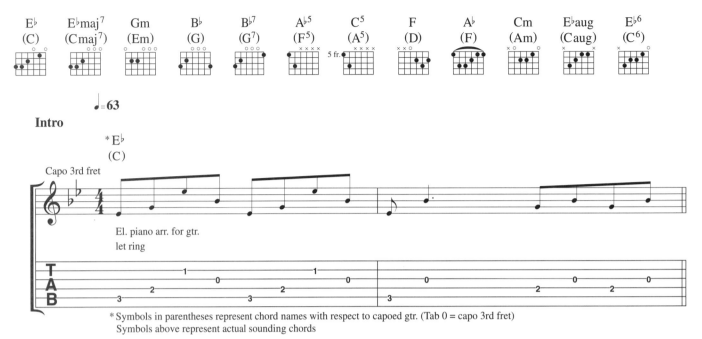

♩ = 63

Intro

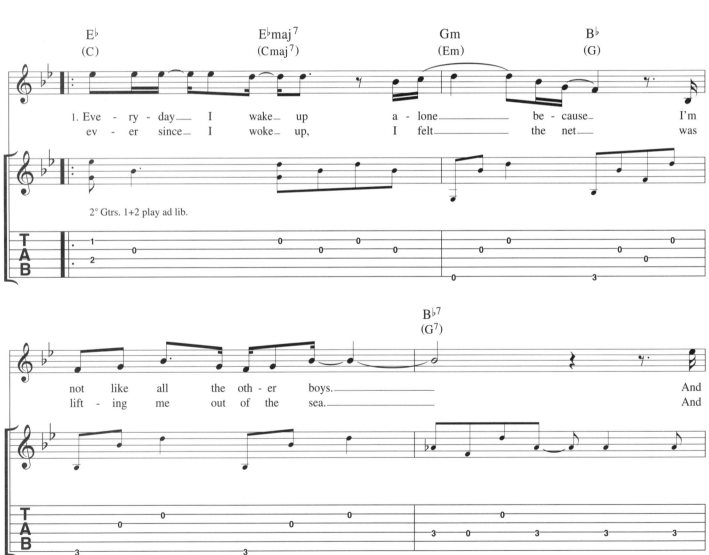

* Symbols in parentheses represent chord names with respect to capoed gtr. (Tab 0 = capo 3rd fret)
Symbols above represent actual sounding chords

1. Eve - ry - day___ I wake__ up a - lone_____ be - cause_ I'm
ev - er since___ I woke__ up, I felt_____ the net___ was

not like all the oth - er boys._____ And
lift - ing me out of the sea._____ And

ev - er since I was young, I had no choice. But
ev - en when I'm sink - ing, I feel the need. But

it's O. K. to lead me on, I must ad - mit it's not much fun, to
it's O. K. to lead me on, I must ad - mit it's not much fun, to

be led on by such a one as
be a - lone with such a one

Gtr. 1 cont. in slashes

21

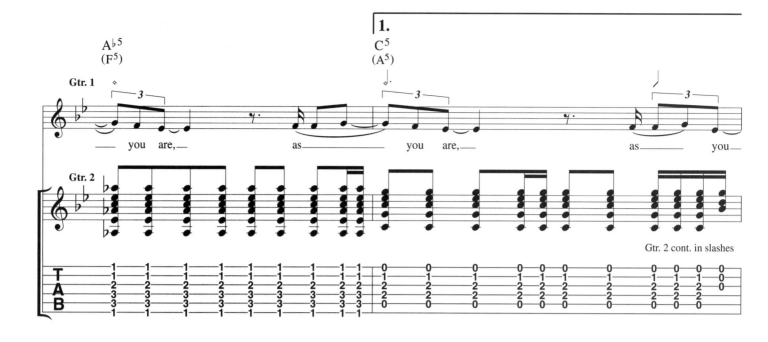

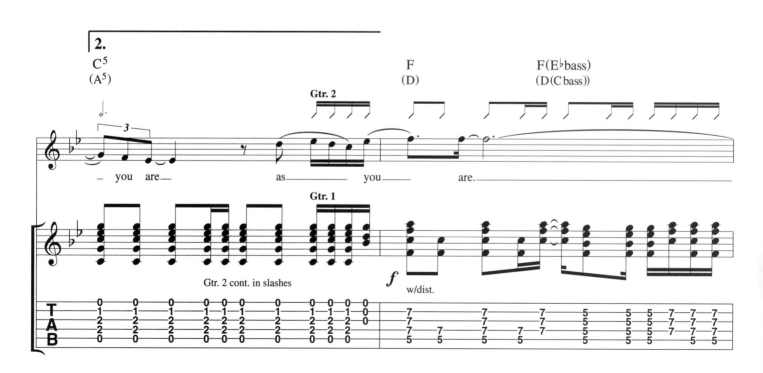

Interlude

Gtr. 3 (elec.)

mf w/clean tone

* Hammer notes and swell w/vol. control

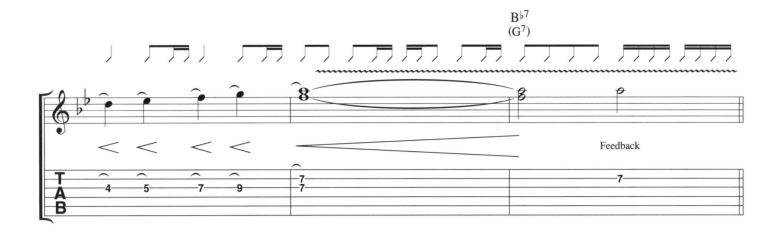

Gtr. solo

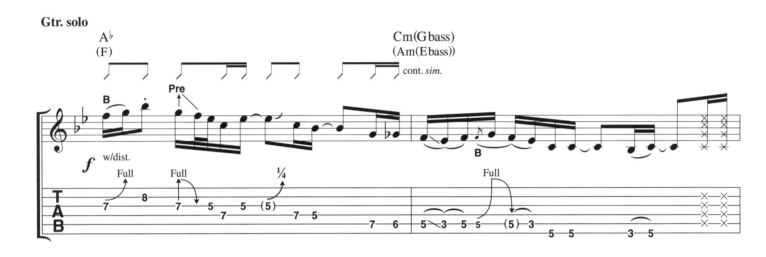

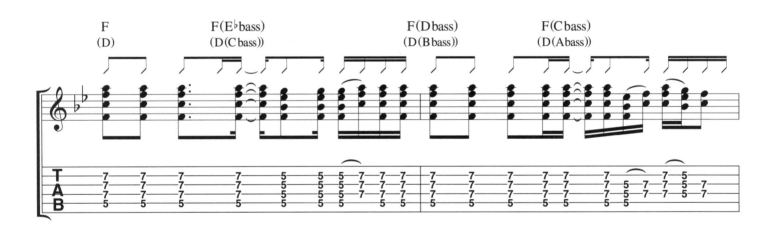

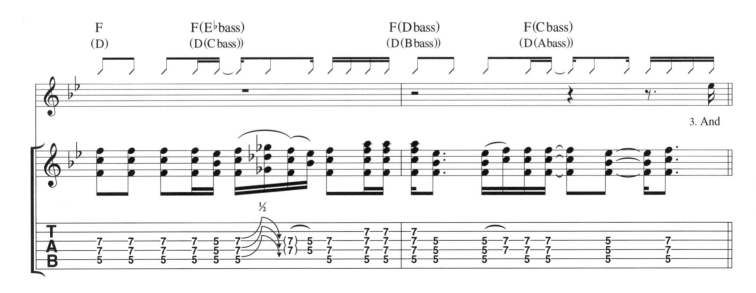

3. And

Verse

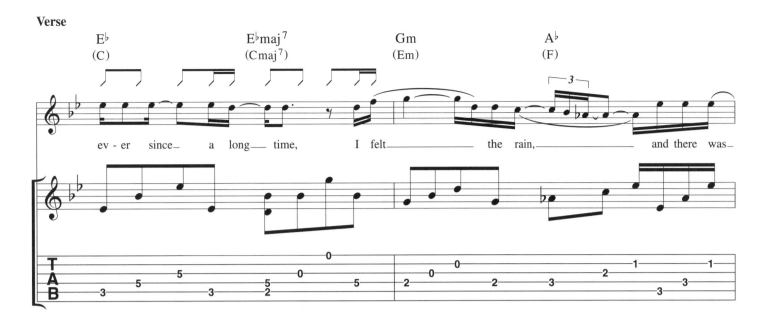

ev - er since a long time, I felt the rain, and there was

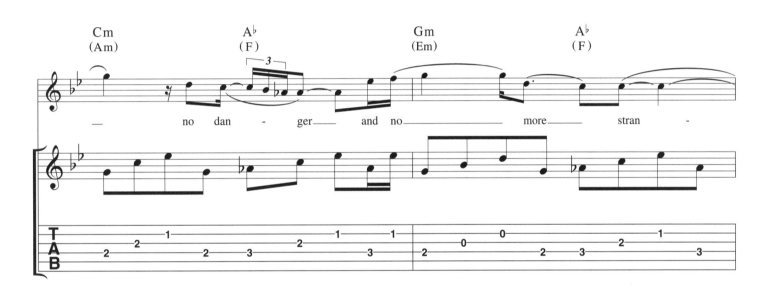

no dan - ger and no more stran -

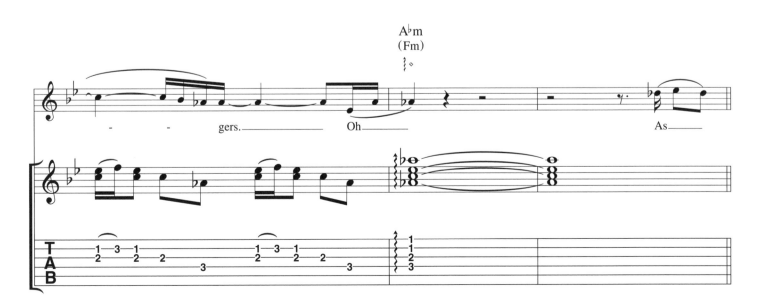

- gers. Oh As

Outro

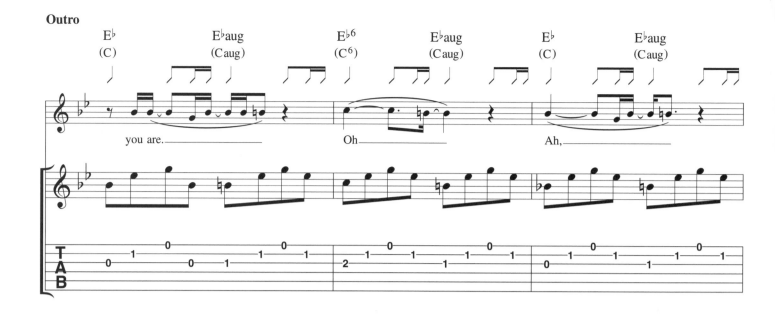

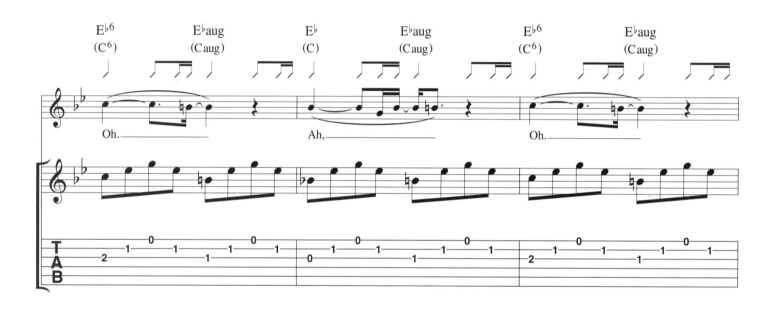

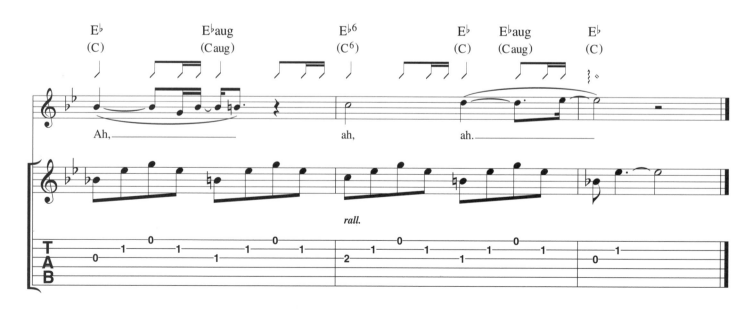

Driftwood

Words & Music by Fran Healy.

Gtrs. 2 + 3 Capo 7th fret

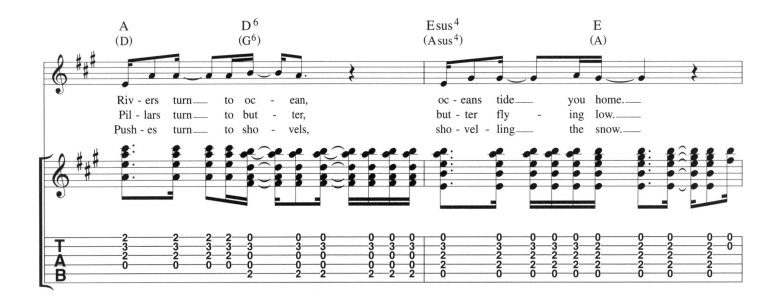

Riv - ers turn___ to oc - ean, oc - eans tide___ you home.___
Pil - lars turn___ to but - ter, but - ter fly - ing low.___
Push - es turn___ to sho - vels, sho - vel - ling___ the snow.___

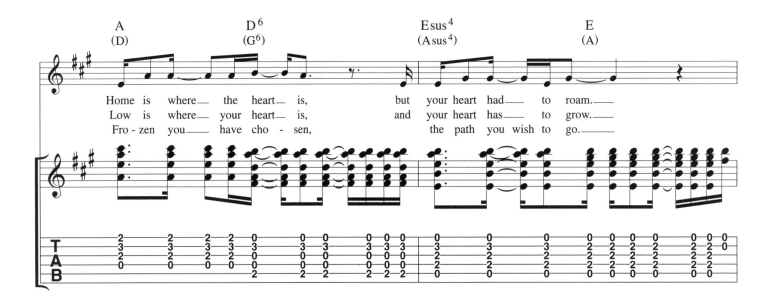

Home is where___ the heart___ is, but your heart had___ to roam.___
Low is where___ your heart___ is, and your heart has___ to grow.___
Fro - zen you___ have cho - sen, the path you wish to go.___

1. 3.

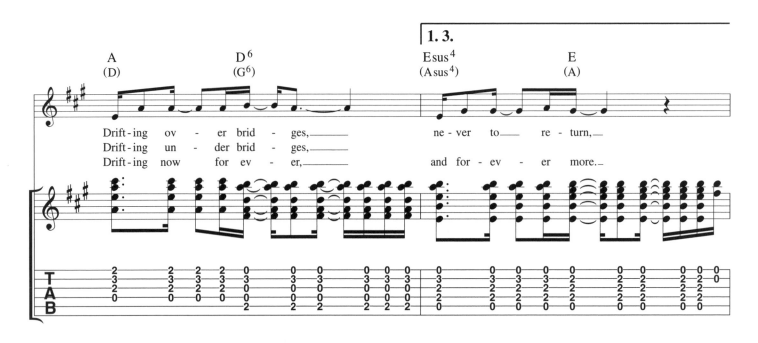

Drift - ing ov - er brid - ges,_____ ne - ver to___ re - turn,
Drift - ing un - der brid - ges,_____
Drift - ing now for ev - er,_____ and for - ev - er more.___

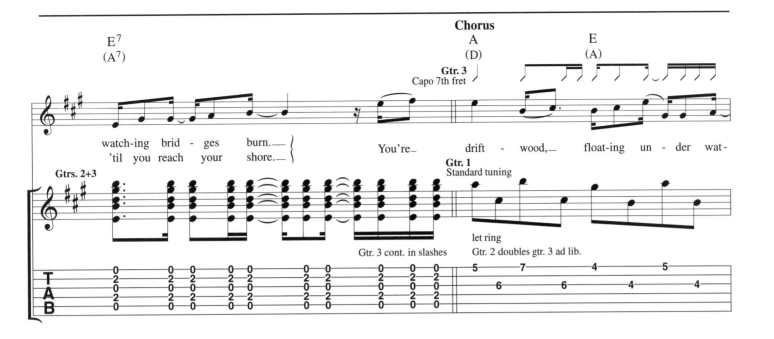

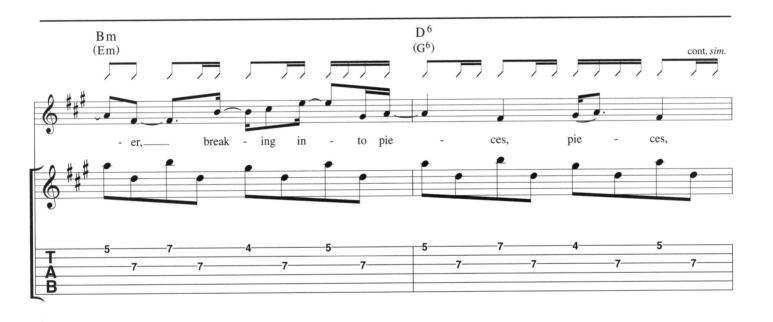

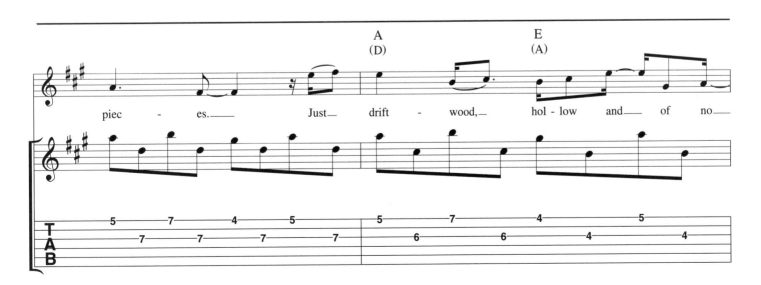

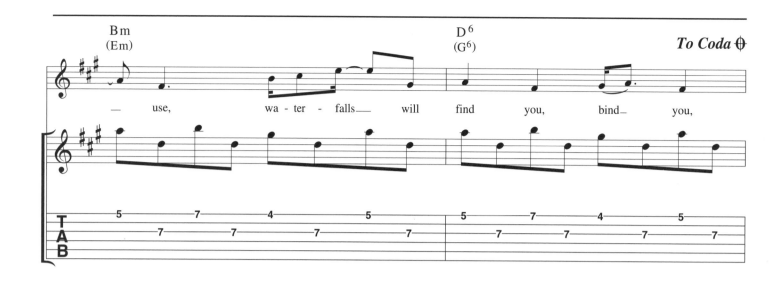

The Last Laugh Of The Laughter

Words & Music by Fran Healy.

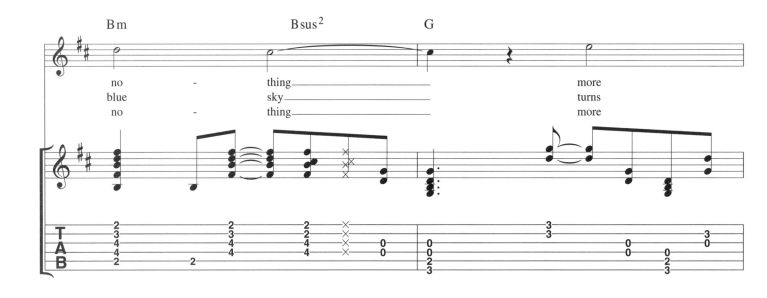

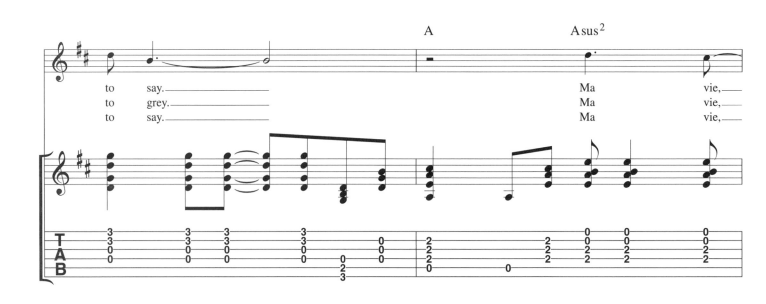

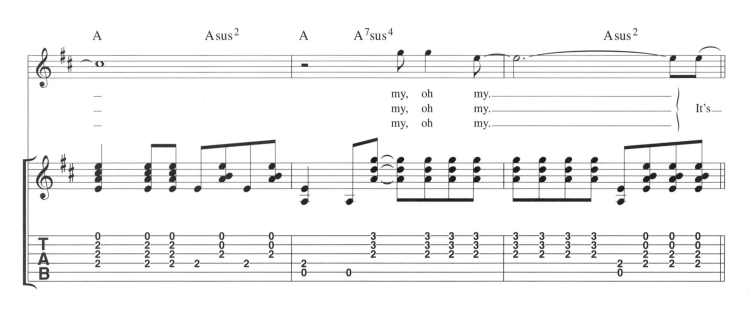

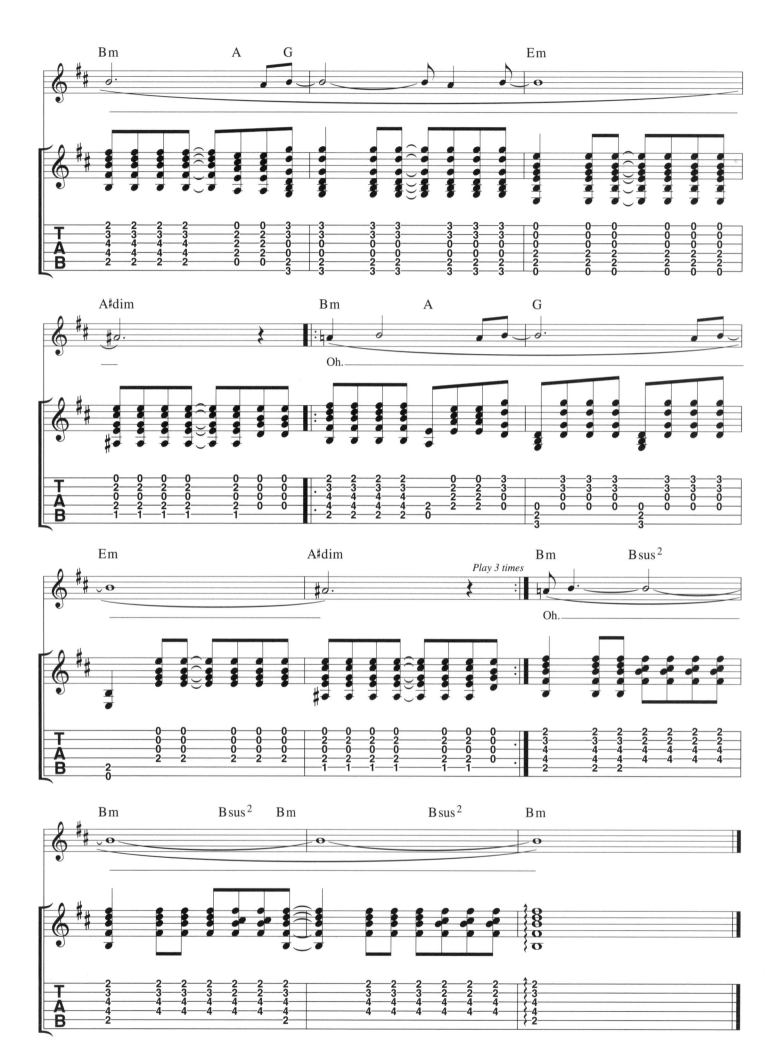

Turn

Words & Music by Fran Healy.

Gtrs 2 + 3 Capo 2nd fret

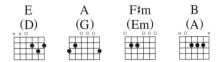

E
(D)

A
(G)

F#m
(Em)

B
(A)

♩=74

Intro

*E
(D)

Gtr. 3 (elec.)
Capo 2nd fret

Gtr. 1 (elec.)
Standard tuning

mf
w/slight dist.
Fig. 1...
Gtr. 2 w/Fig. 2

...Fig. 1 ends

* Symbols in parentheses represent chord names with respect to capoed gtr. (Tab 0 = capo 2nd fret)
Symbols above represent actual sounding chords

Gtr. 2 (acous.)
Capo 2nd fret

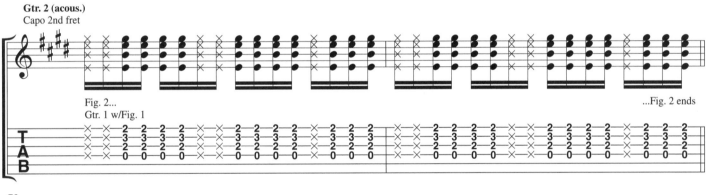

Fig. 2...
Gtr. 1 w/Fig. 1

...Fig. 2 ends

Verse

E
(D)

A
(G)

Gtr. 1

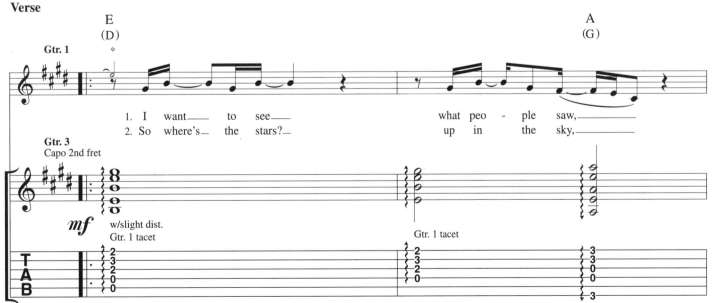

1. I want —— to see ——   what peo - ple saw, ——————
2. So where's — the stars? ——   up in the sky, ——————

Gtr. 3
Capo 2nd fret

mf
w/slight dist.
Gtr. 1 tacet

Gtr. 1 tacet

Pre-Chorus

I want— to sing,————— to sing— my— song.—————
I want— to sing,————— to sing— my— song.—————

Gtr. 3

Gtr. 2 strums ad lib.

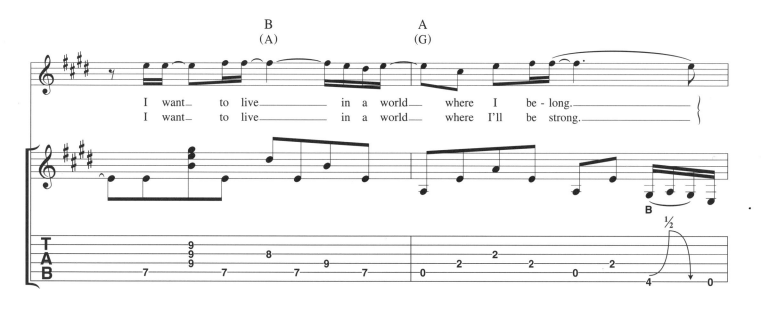

I want— to live————— in a world— where I be-long.—————
I want— to live————— in a world— where I'll be strong.—————

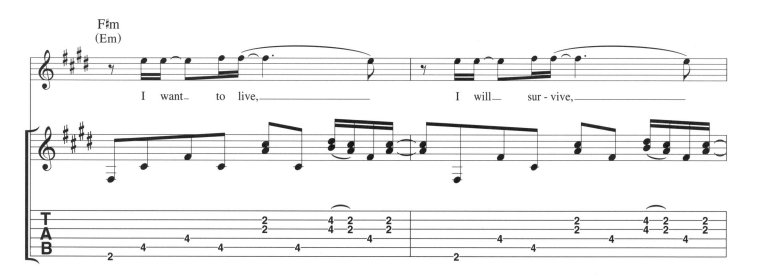

I want— to live,————— I will— sur-vive,—————

44

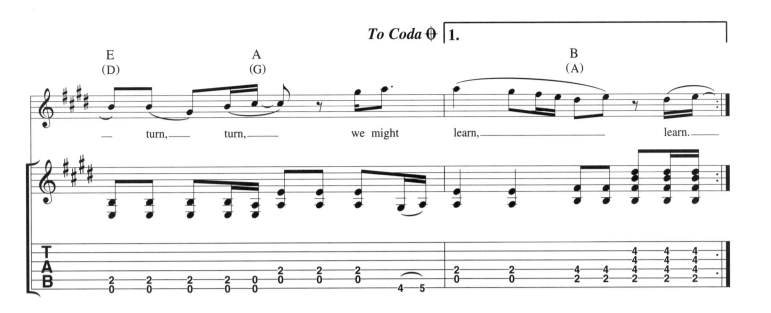

To Coda ⊕ | **1.**

turn,—— turn,—— we might learn,—————————— learn.——

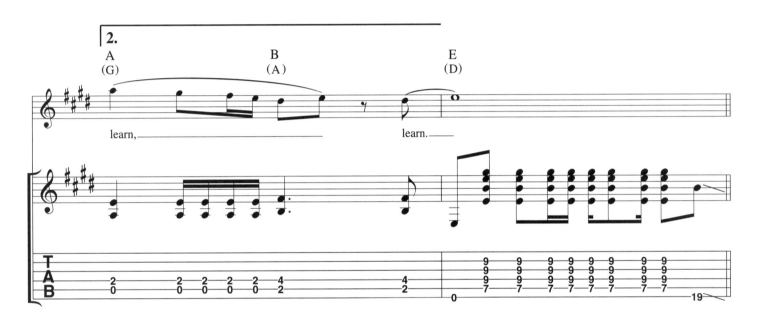

2.

learn,————————————————— learn.————

Bridge

We've got— to turn.—— We've got— to turn.——————

Cont. ad lib.

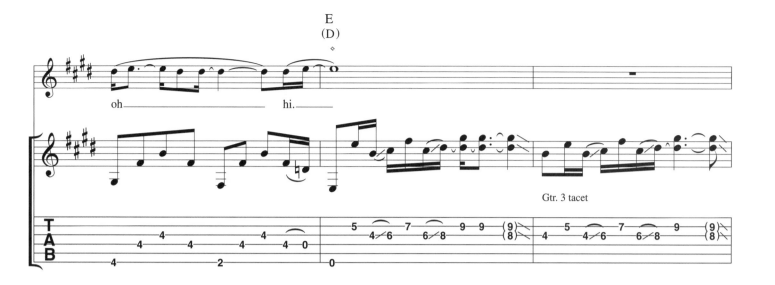

oh_____ hi._____

Gtr. 3 tacet

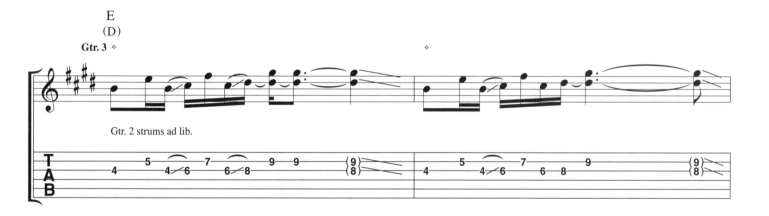

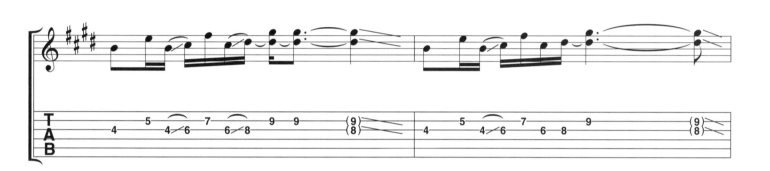

Gtr. 3

Gtr. 2 strums ad lib.

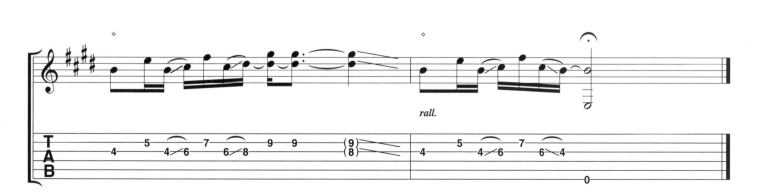

rall.

Why Does It Always Rain On Me?

Words & Music by Fran Healy.

Capo 2nd fret

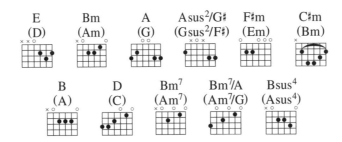

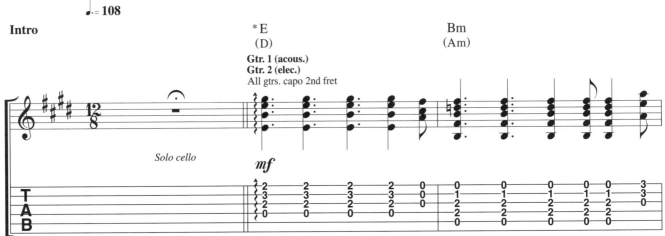

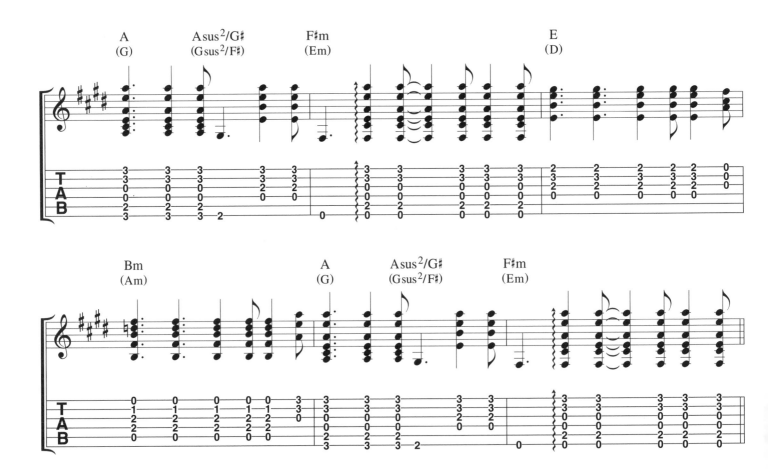

* Symbols in parentheses represent chord names with respect to capoed gtr. (Tab 0 = capo 2nd fret)
Symbols above represent actual sounding chords

Verse

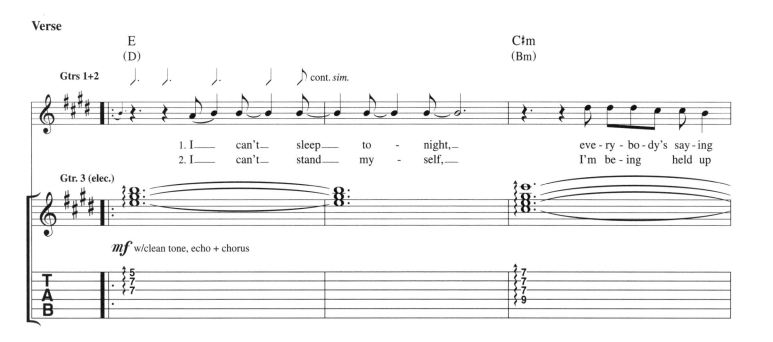

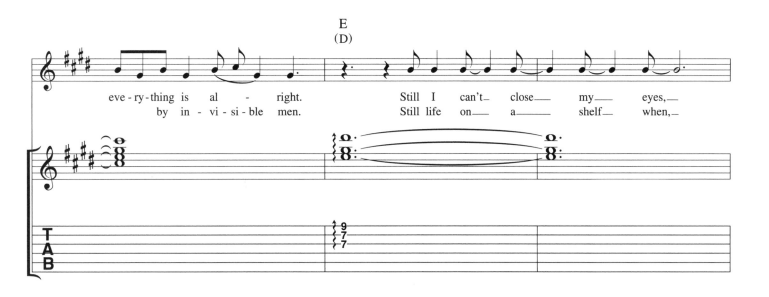

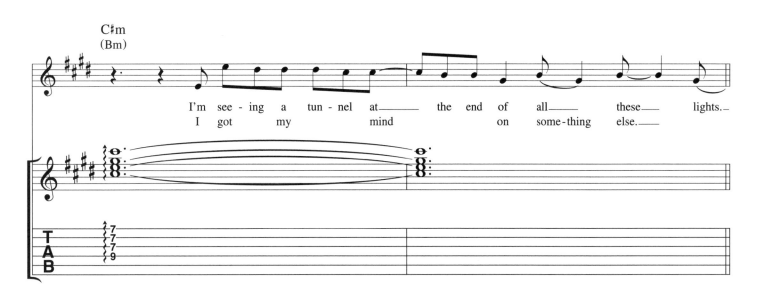

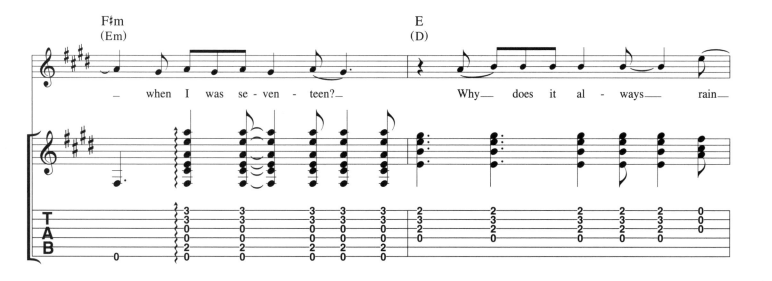

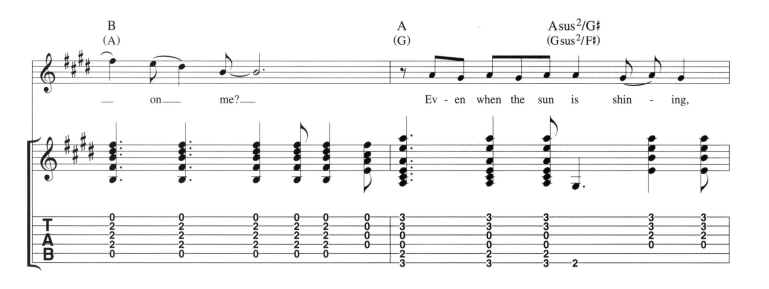

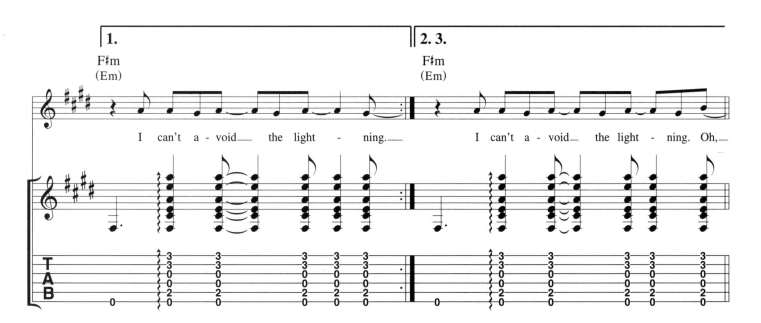

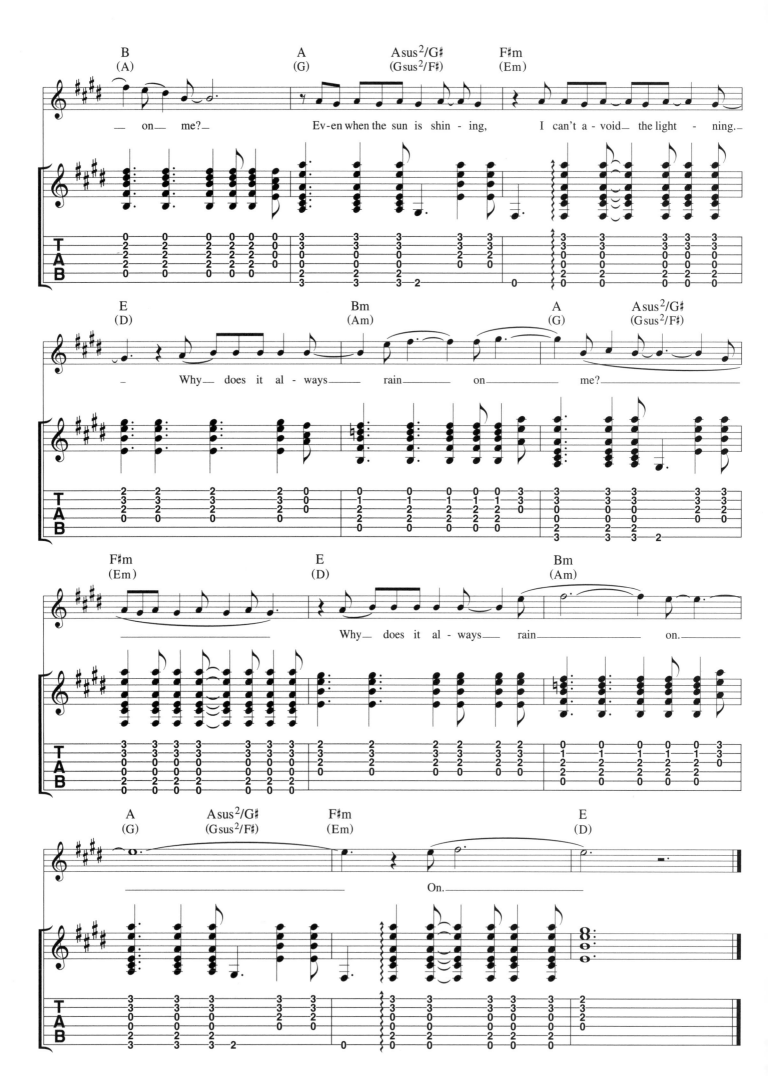

Luv

Words & Music by Fran Healy.

Verse

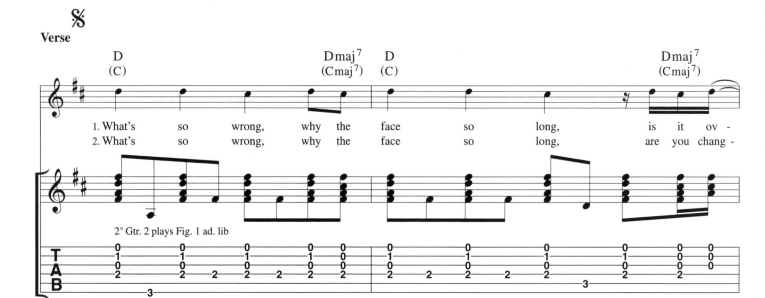

1. What's so wrong, why the face so long, is it ov-
2. What's so wrong, why the face so long, are you chang-

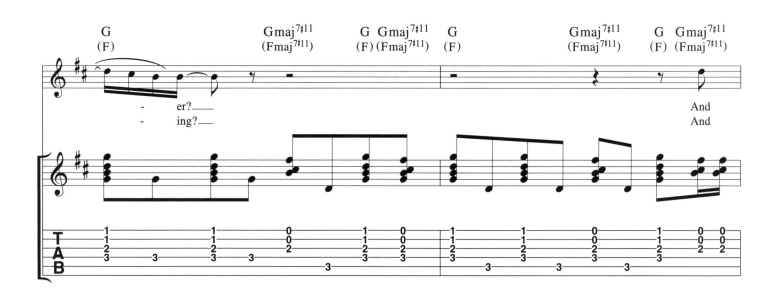

- er?____
- ing?____

And
And

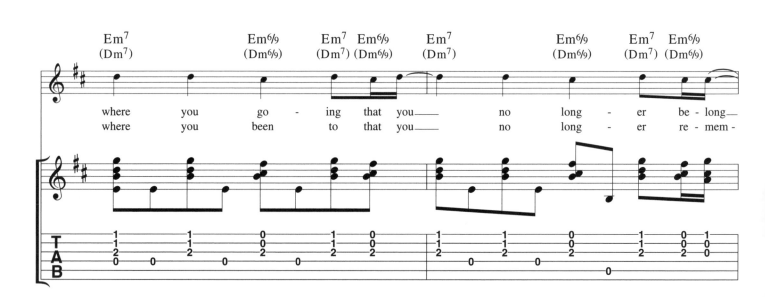

where you go-ing that you____ no long-er be-long____
where you been to that you____ no long-er re-mem-

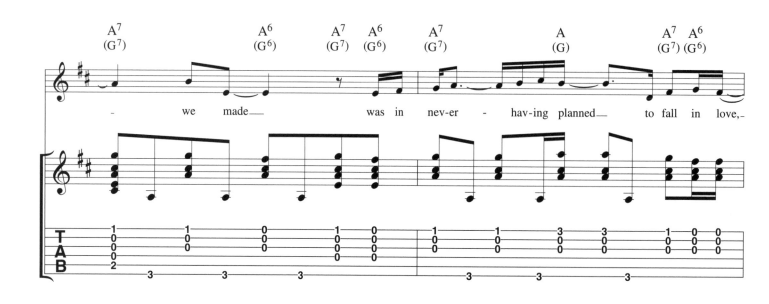

we made___ was in nev-er - hav-ing planned___ to fall in love,-

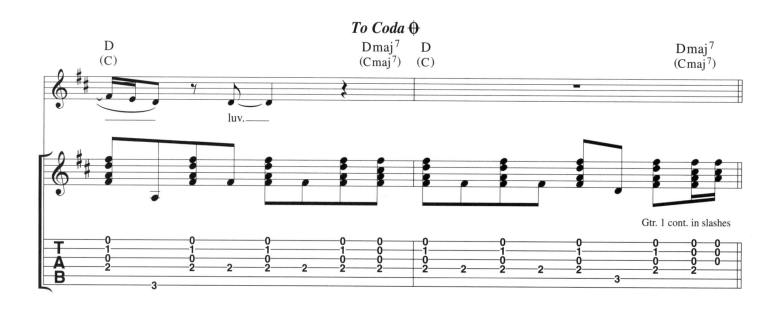

To Coda ⊕

luv.___

Gtr. 1 cont. in slashes

Chorus

Sing - ing this song,___ sing - ing a - long___ makes___ it

Gtr. 1

Gtr. 2 (elec.)
Capo 2nd fret

w/trem. effect

cont. *sim.*

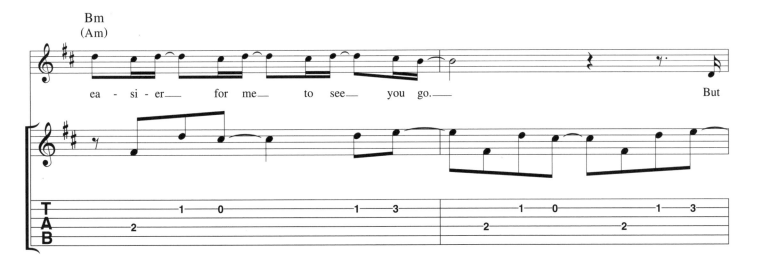

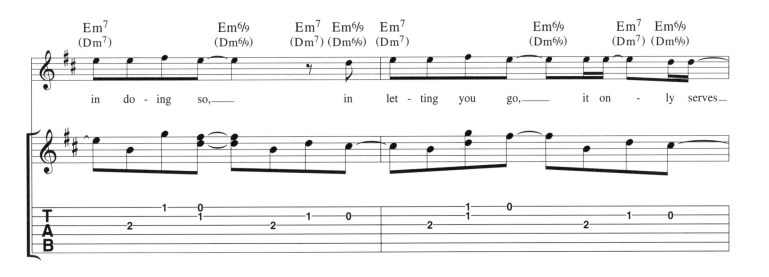

Interlude

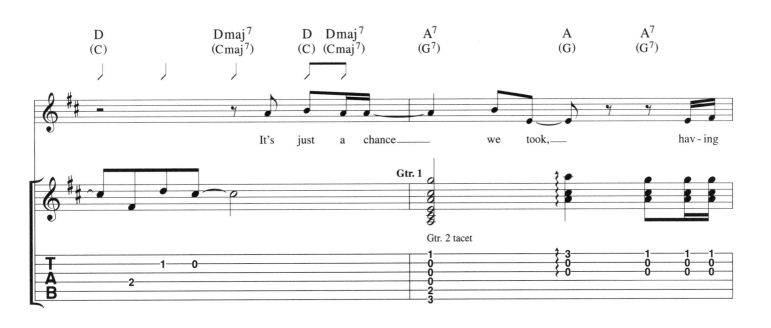

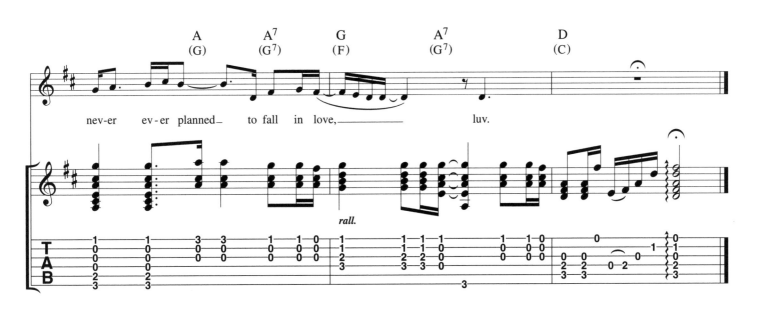

61

Slide Show

Words & Music by Fran Healy.

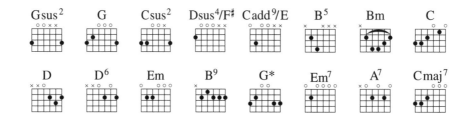

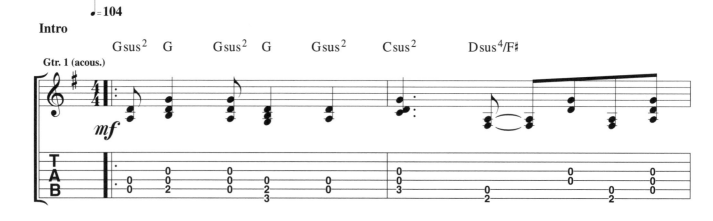

♩=104

Intro

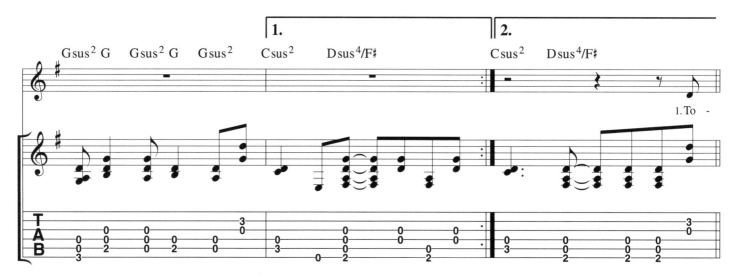

Verse

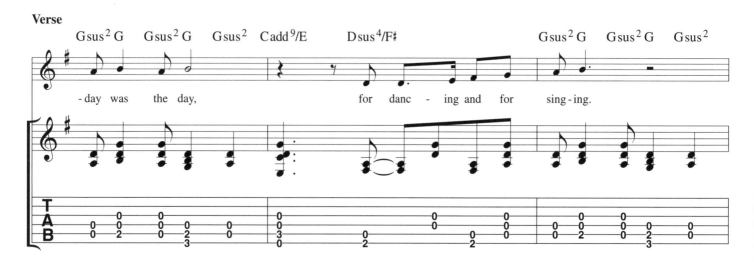

Pre-Chorus

Chorus

65

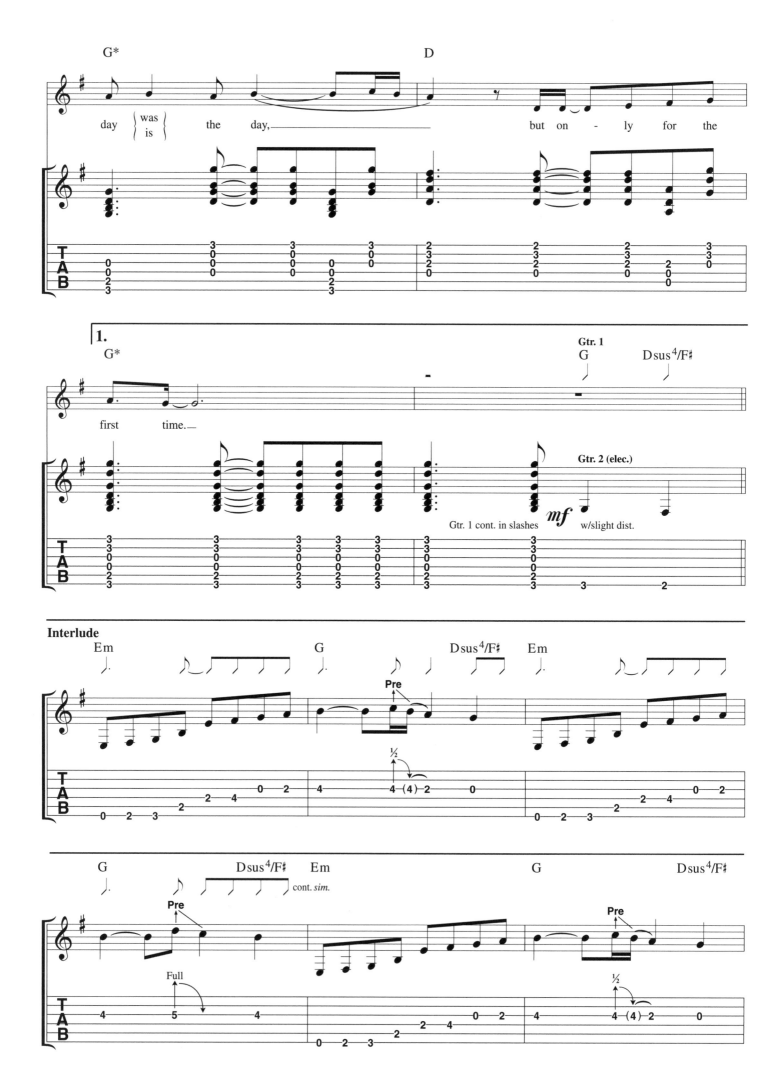

Blue Flashing Light

Words & Music by Fran Healy.

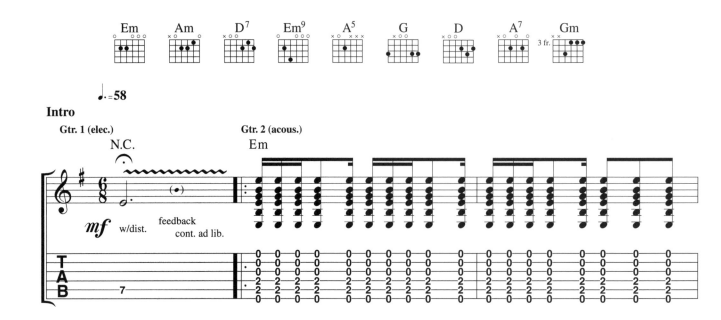

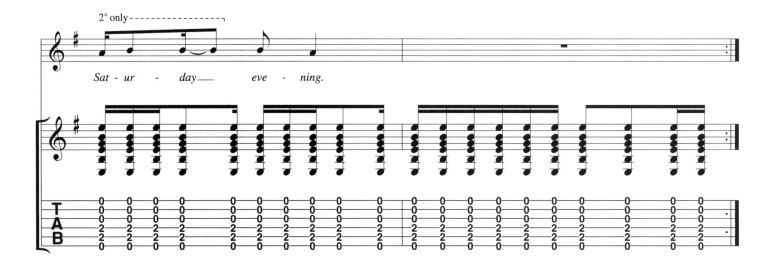

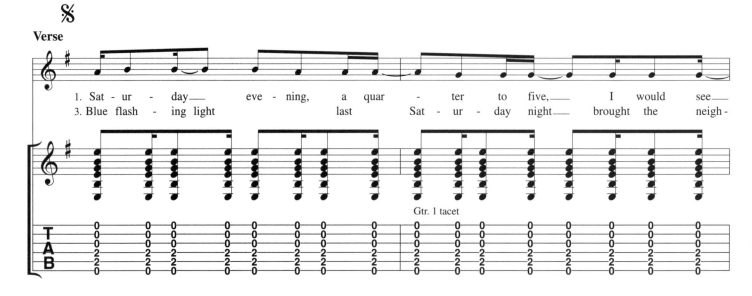

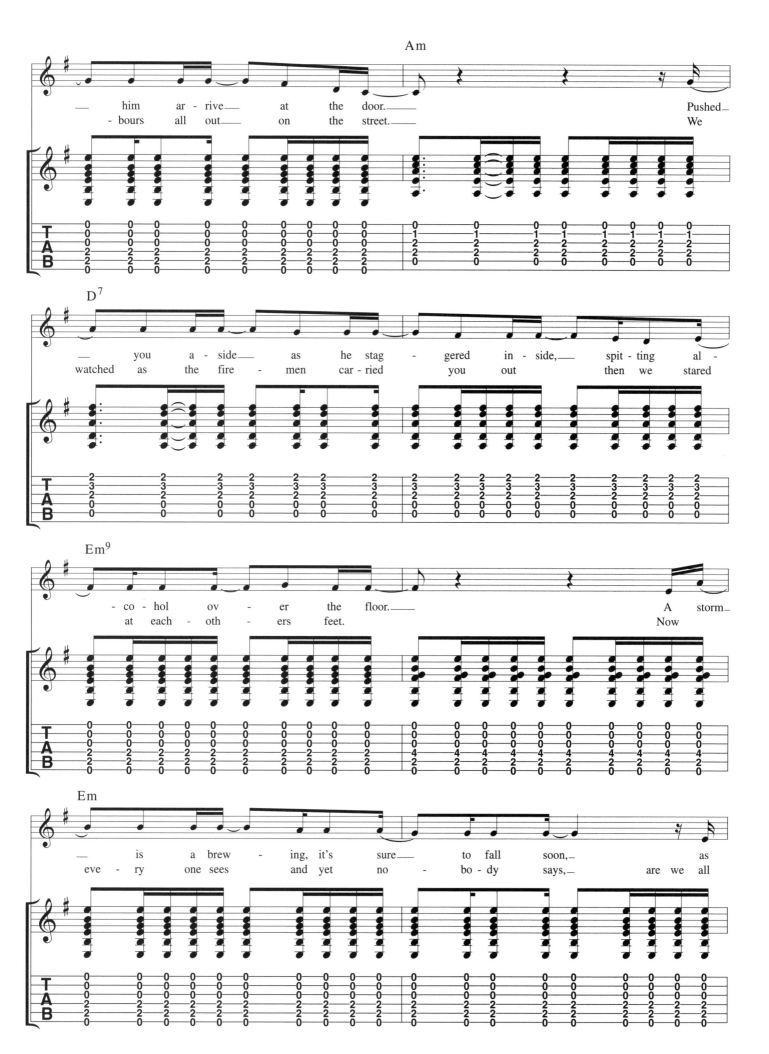

69

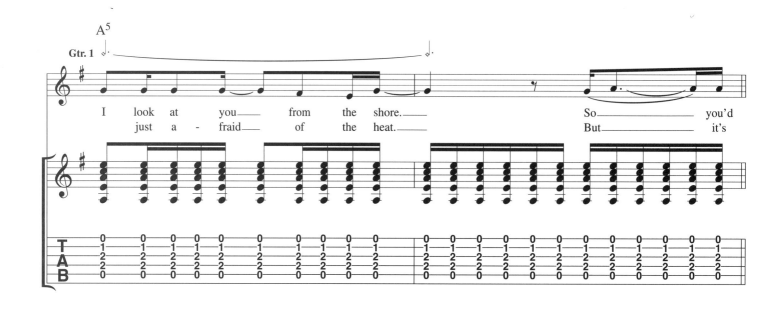

I look at you___ from the shore.___ So___ you'd
just a - fraid___ of the heat.___ But___ it's

Chorus

bet - ter hold___ on___ 'cause it's Sat - ur - day___ night___ and your friends
Sat - ur - day___ night___ at a quar - ter to___ six___ and your friends
Sat - ur - day___ night___ and I'm ly - ing a - lone___ in the bed

— are all out___ and you feel like shit,___ 'cause they
— are all out___ but you live in the sticks,___ still they
— that I made,___ dis - con - nec - ted the phone,___ still they

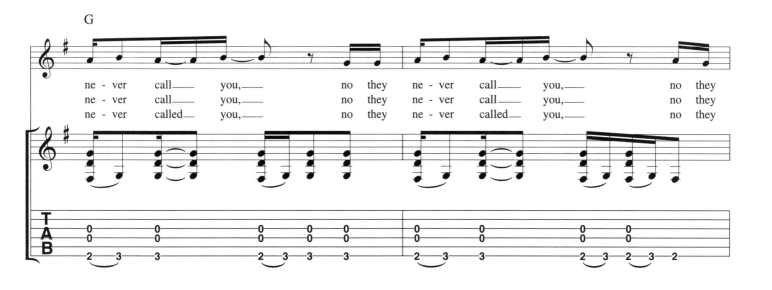

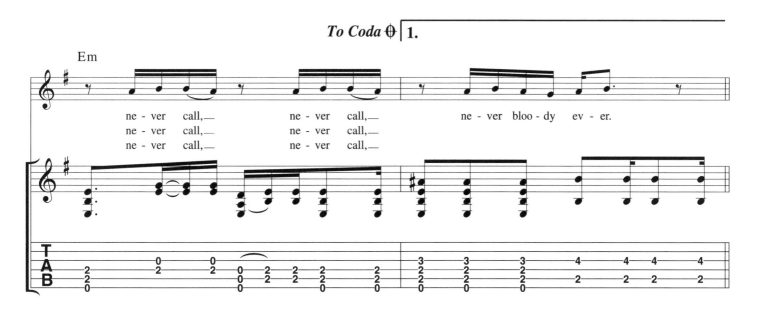

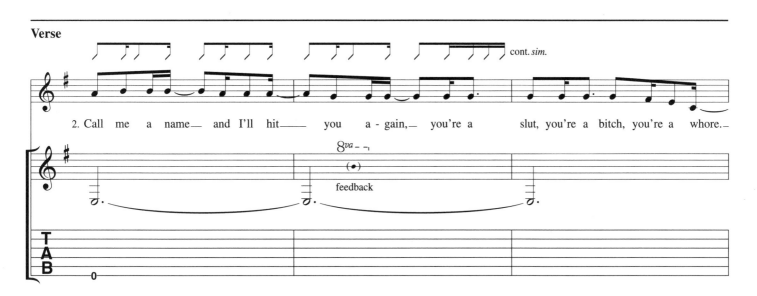

Interlude

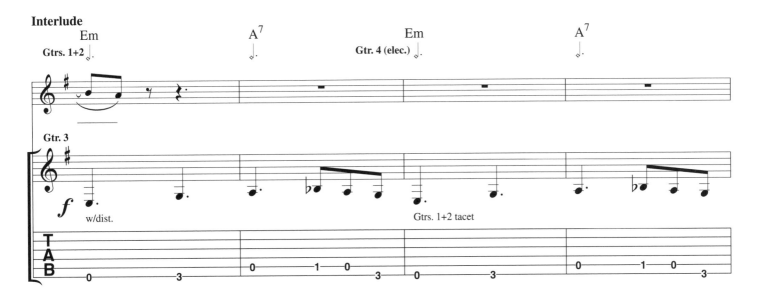

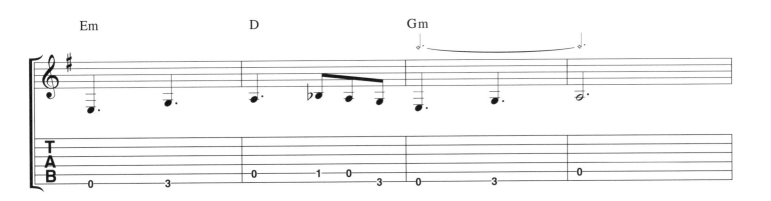

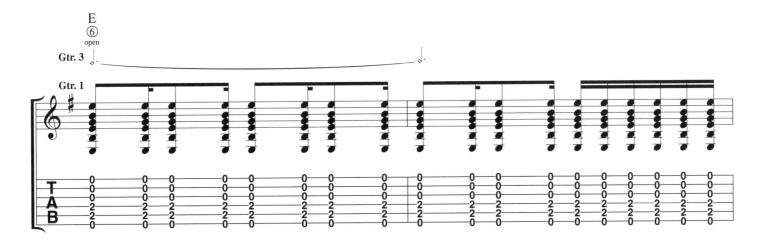

D.%. al Coda

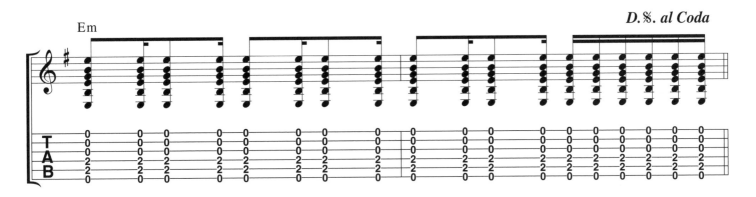

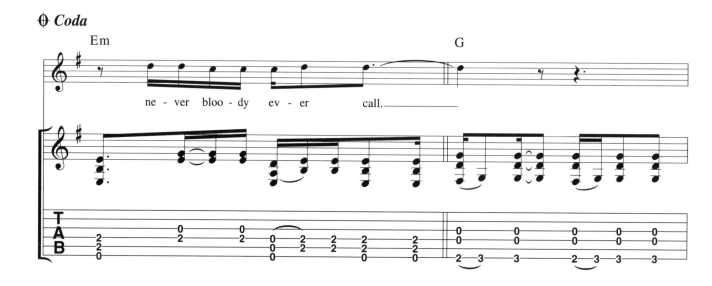

ne - ver bloo - dy ev - er   call.

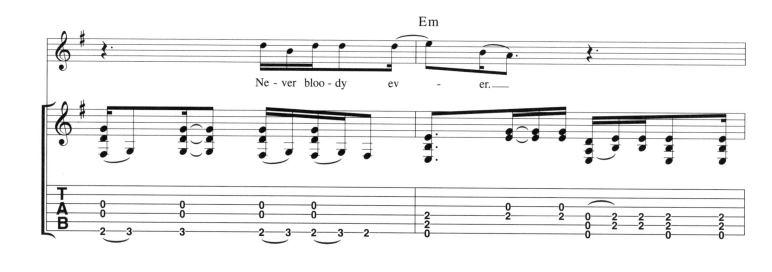

Ne - ver bloo - dy   ev - er.

Ne - ver   do.

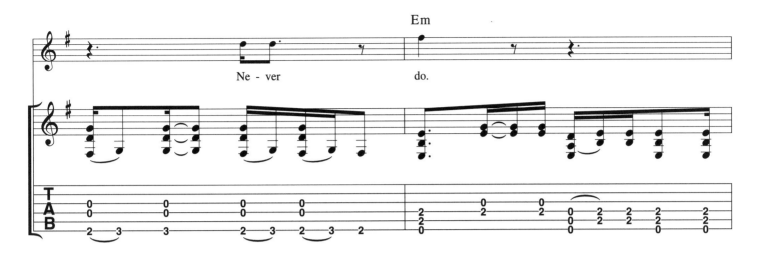

Ne - ver   do.

Em

Outro
Em
Gtr. 4

Gtrs. 1+2

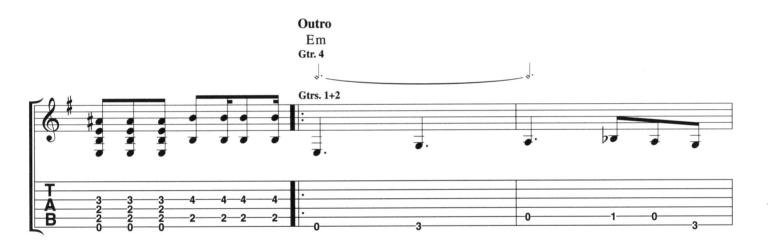

1.   **2.**

Gm
Gtr. 4

Em

Gtrs. 1+2 tacet

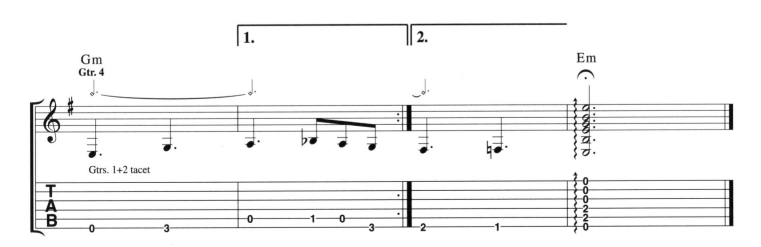

She's So Strange

Words & Music by Fran Healy.

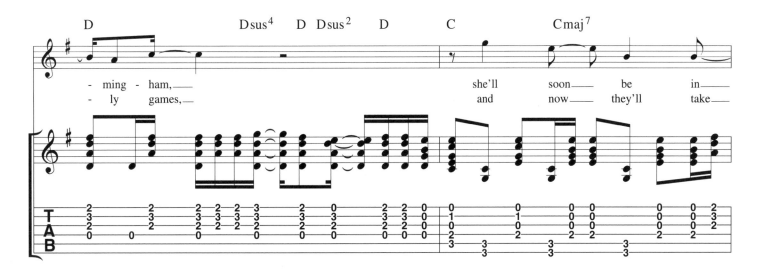

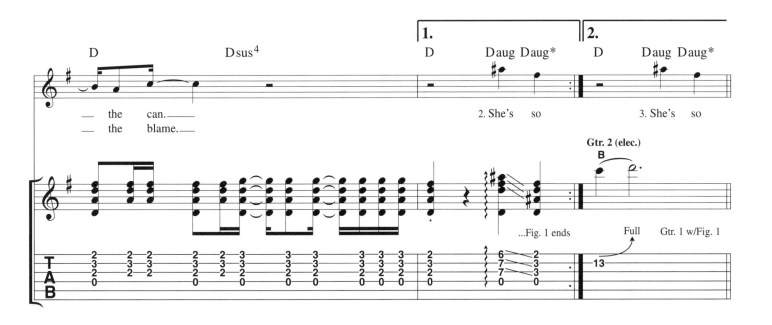

Interlude

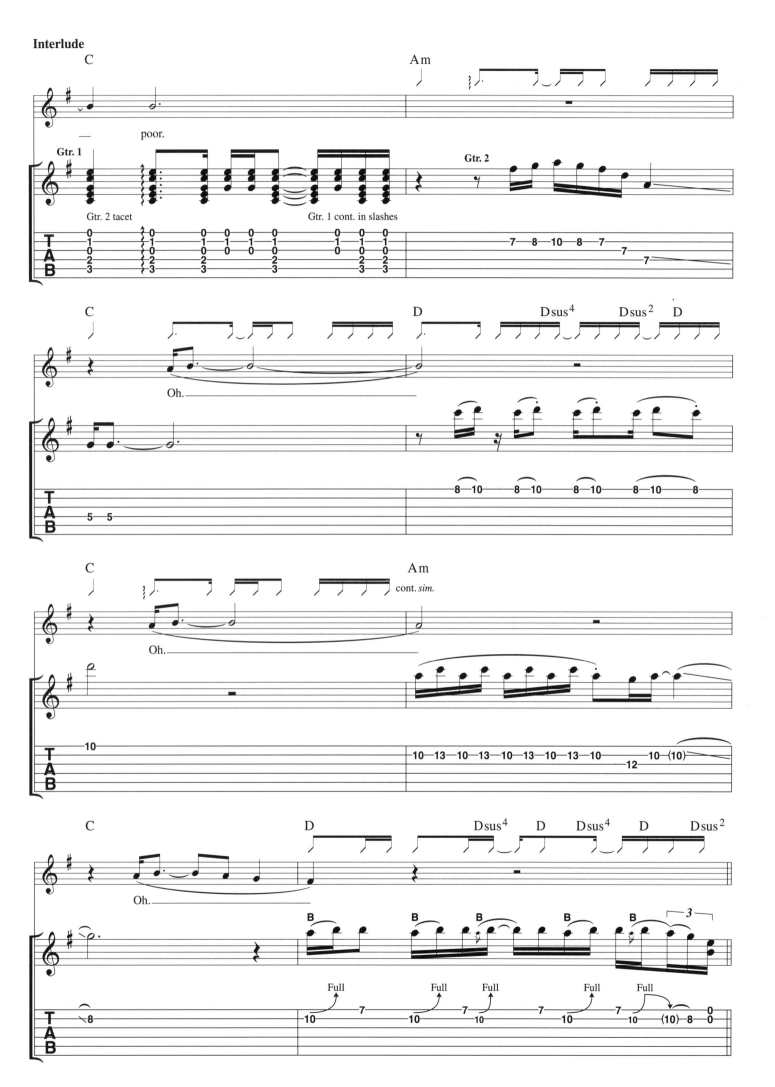

Outro

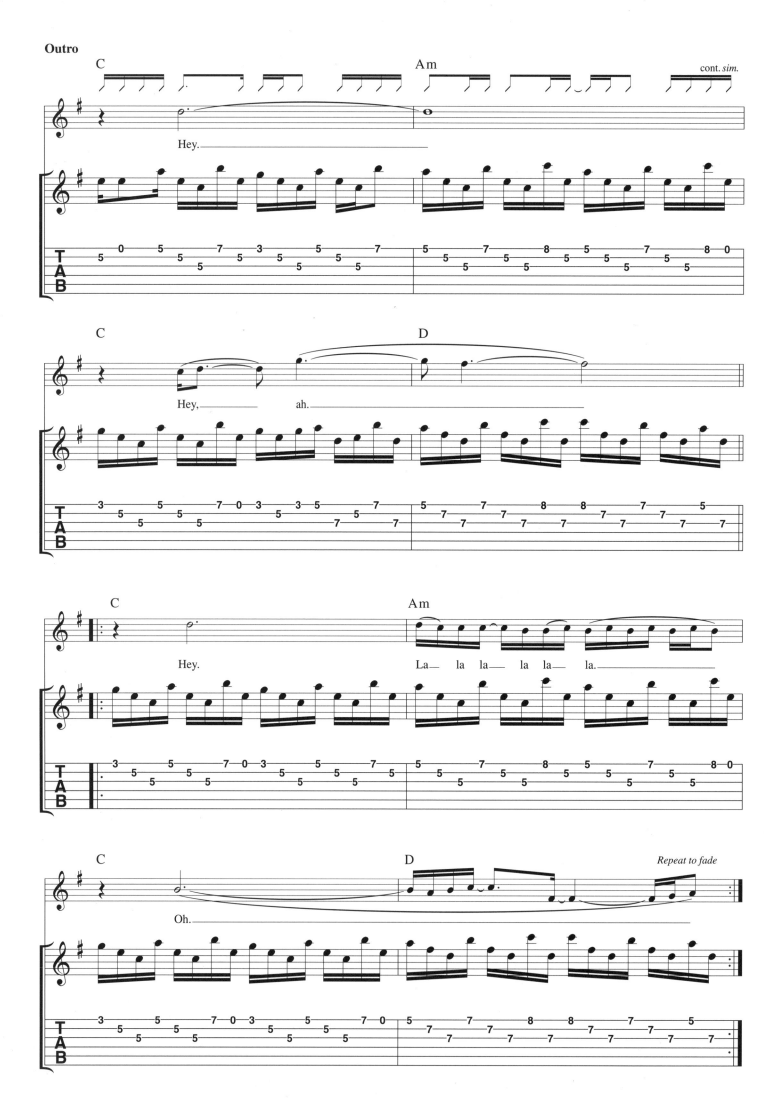

1/02 (42389)